INVESTIGATING
THREE-DIMENSIONAL GEOMETRY

Grades 6 to 12
Key Stages 2 & 3
by
Don Balka

D1217464

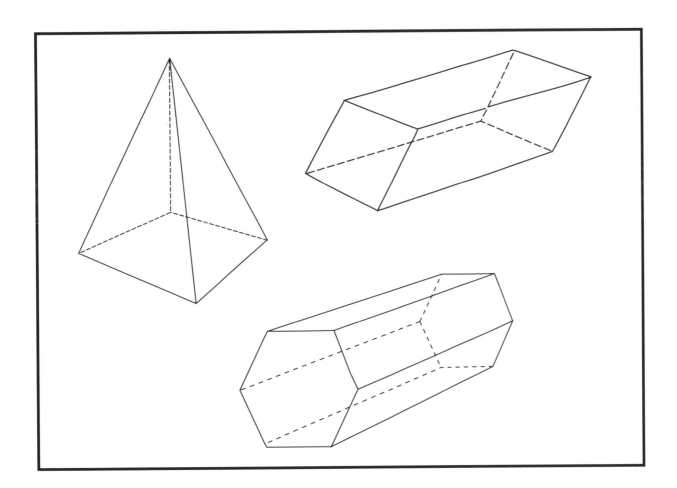

Didax
Educational Resources

CONTENTS

INTRODUCTION

The activities in *Investigating Three-Dimensional Geometry* are designed to be used with the figures contained in the Geometrical Models Kit from Didax Educational Resources and Taskmaster. Made in England, this kit contains a variety of three-dimensional plastic models of figures studied in elementary, middle and high school, plus models of unusual figures such as the oblique pyramid and the oblique cone. Most of the activities will be appropriate for use with ther sets of three-dimensional figures.

As the NCTM *Curriculum and Evaluation Standards for School Mathematics* (1989) state, "Geometric models provide a perspective from which students can analyze and solve problems." With hands-on activities, students are able to investigate and compare the solids, creating their own meaningful definitions of prisms, pyramids, cylinders, cones or other figures. Patterns are provided for students to construct most of the solids contained in the kit.

There are numerous activities for measurement ideas: a brief review of area, slant height, surface area and volume. Number pattern investigations with the geometric figures lead to a study of the algebra of finite differences. Spatial sense activities involve viewing a solid from the top, front and side.

In the paragraphs that follow, you will find information about each of the activities in the book, along with any necessary formulas. To start, let your students investigate the set of models with no formal directions or activities. As they explore, compare, classify and measure three-dimensional figures, they can begin to appreciate the geometry of the real world.

REVIEWING AREA
This page provides a review of the basic area formulas (square, rectangle, triangle and circle). Also included are formulas for special regular polygons that are needed to compute surface areas of some polyhedra.

DIAGONALS OF A POLYGON
The activity is designed for students to discover the pattern for the number of diagonals of a polygon. Integration with the algebra of finite differences provides work on the evaluation of polynomials. The formula for the number of diagonals is $d = n(n - 3)/2$, where **n** is the number of sides of the polygon.

PRISMS AND PYRAMIDS
Identification of and naming prisms and pyramids are the classification ideas presented on these pages. Students are given an opportunity to draw the figures, a difficult task for many.

VERTICES, FACES AND EDGES FOR PRISMS AND PYRAMIDS
Each activity assumes that students understand what a vertex, face and edge is. The

questions lead students to generalizations about the number of vertices, faces and edges for prisms and pyramids.

1. The number of vertices for a prism is twice the number of sides of the shape that is the base.
2. The number of vertices for a pyramid is one more than the number of sides of the shape that is the base.
3. The number of faces for a prism is two more than the number of sides of the shape that is the base.
4. The number of faces for a pyramid is one more than the number of sides of the shape that is the base.
5. The number of edges for a prism is three times the number of sides of the shape that is the base.
6. The number of edges for a prism is twice the number of sides of the shape that is the base.

Follow-up questions can focus on naming a prism or pyramid, given the number of vertices, faces or edges. The activities conclude with questions that lead to Euler's Formula for Solid Figures:

$$\text{Vertices} + \text{Faces} - 2 = \text{Edges}$$

PLATONIC SOLIDS

Work with the regular polyhedra provides opportunities to study early Greek civilization. Patterns are provided for students to construct each polyhedron. The activity can be extended for students to create a variety of non-regular polyhedron using the patterns.

Platonic Solid	Number of Polygons at Each Vertex	
Tetrahedron	3	
Hexahedron	3	
Octahedron	4	
Dodecahedron	3	
Icosahedron	5	

FRUSTUMS

These figures are examples of solids that have been sliced with a cut parallel to the base. The "bottom" part is the frustum. The number of faces for a frustum of a pyramid is two more than the number of sides for the base of the pyramid.

OBLIQUE FIGURES

These unusual figures are often described and drawn in textbooks; however, seldom are models available for students to investigate. For each oblique solid — cylinder and prism — edges connecting base to base are not perpendicular. For each oblique solid

INTRODUCTION

— pyramid and cone — line segments connecting the apex to midpoint of the base are not perpendicular.

NAMING A POLYHEDRON
A polyhedron can be named by the shape of its base(s) or by the number of faces it has. Some polyhedra have additional names. For example, a cube could be named as a rectangular prism or regular hexahedron; an oblique rectangular prism is sometimes called a parallelepiped.

FIND THE SOLID
This activity for small groups incorporates various clues about a three-dimensional figure for students to use in finding the solid. Have students create their own sets of clues for some of the figures.

EULER'S FORMULA
Described earlier for prisms and pyramids, this activity provides students an opportunity to discover the same formula for the Platonic Solids. Since vertices and edges are involved, the formula does not work for cylinders and cones.

NAME CHANGE
This activity is an extension of **Naming a Polyhedron**. Further extensions could include determining the name of a polyhedron by the number of vertices. For example, a polyhedron with six vertices could be a triangular prism, pentagonal pyramid or octahedron.

DIHEDRAL ANGLES
Dihedral angles are often called "space angles" because they are three-dimensional angles. Students can use protractors to measure them.

Polyhedron	Measure	
Cube	90°	
Triangular Prism	90°	60°
Hexagonal Prism	90°	120°
Octagonal Prism	90°	135°
Triangular Pyramid	60°	
Square Pyramid	75°	30°
Hexagonal Pyramid	75°	30°

INTERIOR DIAGONAL OF RECTANGULAR PRISMS
Finding the length of an interior diagonal of a rectangular prism requires the use of the Pythagorean Theorem twice. For cubes, a pattern emerges. The length of a diagonal of a face is $s\sqrt{2}$, where s is the length of a side; the length of an interior diagonal of a cube is $s\sqrt{3}$. A cube with a side of 3 units has an interior diagonal of length $3\sqrt{3}$; a cube with a side of 4 units has an interior diagonal of length $4\sqrt{3}$; a cube with a side of x

INTRODUCTION

units has an interior diagonal of length $x\sqrt{3}$. For the rectangular prism (5 x 5 x 10 cm) in the set of geometric models, the interior diagonal has a length of $5\sqrt{6}$ **cm**. For a rectangular prism with dimensions of a x b x c, the interior diagonal has a length of $D = \sqrt{a^2 + b^2 + c^2}$.

DIAGONALS OF PRISMS
This activity involves finding the number of diagonals for a variety of prisms and discovering a pattern to determine the number.

Prism	Number of Interior Diagonals
Triangular	0 = 0 x 3
Rectangular	4 = 1 x 4
Pentagonal	10 = 2 x 5
Hexagonal	18 = 3 x 6
Heptagonal	28 = 4 x 7
Octagonal	40 = 5 x 8
Nonagonal	54 = 6 x 9
Decagonal	70 = 7 x 10

In general, the number of interior diagonals for a prism with a base that has **n** sides is **n x (n – 3)**.

SIMILARITIES AND DIFFERENCES
Classifying the geometric solids by different characteristics is the major focus of this activity. Once sorted, students can describe similarities and differences. The activity lends itself to writing assignments.

SLANT HEIGHTS OF PYRAMIDS AND CONES
The study of slant heights is necessary to find lateral and total surface areas of three-dimensional figures. Although this activity involves using a ruler to measure the slant heights for a right square pyramid and a right circular cone, students familiar with the Pythagorean Theorem can form right triangles to find the exact values of the slant heights. For the pyramid and cone in the kit, the slant height is $\sqrt{106.25}$ **cm**.

TOTAL SURFACE AREA FOR PRISMS
Students are carefully led to a general formula for finding the total surface area of any prism, **TSA = 2 x Area of Base + Sum of Areas of Parallelograms**. Total surface areas for each prism can be found in the table on page 64.

TOTAL SURFACE AREA FOR PYRAMIDS
Slant height now becomes useful in finding the total surface area of a pyramid, since it becomes the altitude (height) of a triangular face. Total surface areas for each pyramid can be found in the table on page 64.

INTRODUCTION

SURFACE AREA OF A SPHERE AND HEMISPHERE

Unlike prisms and pyramids, calculus is necessary to develop the formula for the total surface area of a sphere. If the radius of a sphere is doubled, the total surface area is quadrupled. For a hemisphere, $\textbf{TSA} = 3\pi r^2$.

SURFACE AREA FOR A CYLINDER

For any right circular cylinder, the total surface area is given by the formula $\textbf{TSA} = 2\pi r^2 + 2\pi rh$, where **r** is the radius of the circular base and **h** is the height of the cylinder. Students need to see the "unwrapped" curved surface of a cylinder as they investigate surface area. This surface is outlined on page 39.

SURFACE AREA OF A CONE

Developing the formula for the total surface area of a cone involves several steps. Students also need to see the "unwrapped" curved surface of a cone. This surface is outlined on page 39. By visualizing this surface, they can work with it as a sector of a large circle. The area of the lateral surface is $\textbf{2.5}\pi\sqrt{\textbf{106.25}}$.

GEOJACKETS

Geojackets are useful in determining the total surface area of three-dimensional figures. With the figures in the set of geometric models having metric lengths, most of the geojackets are easy to measure and construct. Students can use formulas for the areas of squares, rectangles and triangles to find total surface areas. As an extension of this activity, provide students with dimensions of cubes or rectangular prisms and let them construct geojackets. Tape can be used to complete the figures.

VOLUME OF A PRISM AND A CYLINDER

The formula for the volume of any prism or cylinder can be generalized:

V = Area of base x Height

For a cube, the formula is simple $\textbf{V} = \textbf{s}^3$, where **s** is the length of a side. If the length of a side is doubled, the volume of the new cube is eight times that of the original cube. Opportunities are provided in this activity for students to describe how to find the volume of various figures.

VOLUME OF A PYRAMID AND A CONE

Just as the general formula for the volume of any prism or cylinder is the same, so is the general formula for the volume of a pyramid or cone.

V = 1/3 x Area of base x Height

The geojacket patterns provide students with an opportunity to discover this relationship. Have students construct the geojackets for the rectangular prism, square pyramid, cylinder and cone. Omit one base for each as they are taped together. Students can use sand, rice or some other material to fill the pyramid and transfer the contents to the rectangular prism. As the formula shows, it will be necessary to fill the pyramid three times in order to fill the rectangular prism. Repeat the process with the cone and cylinder.

VOLUME OF A SPHERE AND A HEMISPHERE

Again, calculus is needed to develop the formula for the volume of a sphere

$$V = 4/3\pi r^3, \text{ where } r \text{ is the radius of the sphere.}$$

If the radius is doubled, the volume is eight times the volume of the original sphere. This is the same relationship that existed for a cube when a side was doubled. The volume of a hemisphere is one-half the volume of a sphere.

STELLATED POLYHEDRA

By taping pyramids on each face of a polyhedron, a "star-like" polyhedron is created. Pages are provided with the appropriate number of shapes to create pyramids for each of the faces of the Platonic Solids. The completed figures make interesting objects for mobiles or Christmas tree decorations.

DIFFERENT VIEWS

When viewing a three-dimensional object from different views, various two-dimensional shapes appear. This activity focuses on views from the top, front and right side of several geometric shapes. Students can also create views for models not provided on the pages.

CROSS SECTIONS

When a cube is sliced with a slice parallel to a base, a square is observed. If one vertex of a cube is sliced away, the resulting plane region is a triangle. Students are given an opportunity to describe other possible slices on a cube and the resulting polygonal regions. Similar activities are provided using a cylinder, square pyramid and cone.

CUTTING CORNERS

This activity is an extension of the activity for the volume of a rectangular prism. Students need to cut out the grids and corner squares to form boxes without lids. By finding the volumes of each box, students can determine the integral dimensions of the box with greatest volume. Later work in calculus will show students how to find the exact values for maximum volume.

APPROXIMATE SURFACE AREAS AND VOLUMES

This page provides approximate values for total surface area and volume for most of the figures in the Geometrical Models Kit. Special formulas not covered in this book have been used in some cases.

Don Balka

GEOMETRICAL MODELS KIT

Below is a list of the 25 models contained in the Geometrical Models Kit (5-361) available from Didax Educational Resources (USA) and Taskmaster (England).

1. Regular Tetrahedron
2. Regular Hexahedron (Cube)
3. Regular Octahedron
4. Regular Icosahedron
5. Regular Dodecahedron
6. Cylinder
7. Square Pyramid
8. Cone
9. Rectangular Prism
10. Sphere
11. Frustum of a Cylinder
12. Frustum of a Square Pyramid
13. Frustum of a Cone
14. Frustum of a Square Prism
    (Trapezoidal Prism)
15. Hemisphere
16. Oblique Cylinder
17. Oblique Square Pyramid
18. Oblique Cone
19. Oblique Square Prism
    (Parallelepiped)
20. Ovoid
21. Octagonal Prism
22. Hexagonal Pyramid
23. Trapezoidal Prism
24. Triangular Prism
25. Hexagonal Prism

investigating
THREE-DIMENSIONAL
geometry

REVIEWING AREA

Finding the area of polygons, circles, and other two-dimensional figures is necessary in order to find the surface area (or total surface area) of three-dimensional figures. Here is a review of some of the area formulas you have studied. Use the polygonal and circular shapes in your set of geometric models to practice finding areas. Blank spaces are provided below for you to list various measurements and to find the areas.

SQUARE	RECTANGLE	TRIANGLE
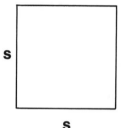	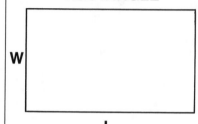	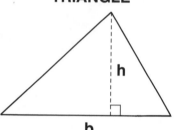
$A = s^2$	$A = L \times W$	$A = 1/2\ b \times h$
$s = \underline{\hspace{1cm}}$	$L = \underline{\hspace{1cm}}$ $W = \underline{\hspace{1cm}}$	$b = \underline{\hspace{1cm}}$ $h = \underline{\hspace{1cm}}$
$A = \underline{\hspace{1cm}}$	$A = \underline{\hspace{1cm}}$	$A = \underline{\hspace{1cm}}$

There is a special formula for finding the area of an equilateral triangle. It can also be used to find the area of a regular hexagon.

CIRCLE

$A = \pi r^2$

$r = \underline{\hspace{2cm}}$

$A = \underline{\hspace{2cm}}$

EQUILATERAL TRIANGLE

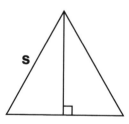

$A = \sqrt{3/4}\ s^2$

$s = \underline{\hspace{1cm}}$ $A = \underline{\hspace{1.5cm}}$

REGULAR HEXAGON

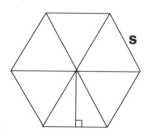

$A = 6\sqrt{3/4}\ s^2$

$s = \underline{\hspace{1cm}}$ $A = \underline{\hspace{1.5cm}}$

Some of the three-dimensional figures have regular pentagons, regular hexagons or regular octagons as faces. There is a general formula for finding the area of any regular polygon.

A = 1/4 ns^2 cot (180°/n), where

n = number of sides of the regular polygon, and

s = length of side of regular polygon

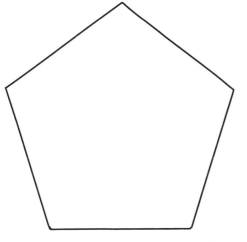

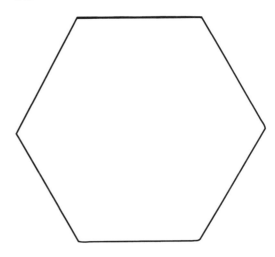

s = _____   A = _____   s = _____   A = _____

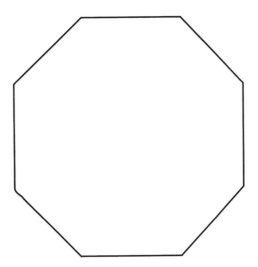

s = _____   A = _____

CAN YOU FIND A PATTERN?
DIAGONALS OF A POLYGON

A **Diagonal of a Polygon** is a line segment joining any two non-adjacent vertices. Find the number of diagonals for each polygon shown below. Record your results and complete the table below.

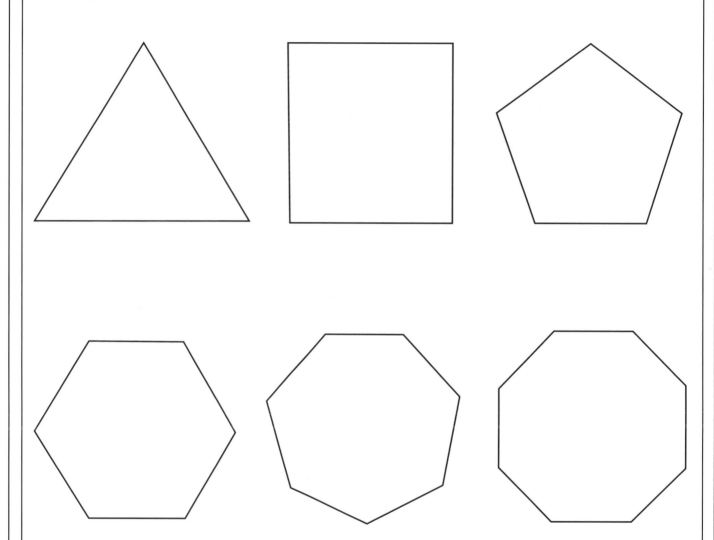

NUMBER OF SIDES	3	4	5	6	7	8	9	10
NUMBER OF DIAGONALS								

PRISMS

A **PRISM** is one type of polyhedron. It is a solid figure with at least one pair of faces that are parallel and congruent. The remaining faces are parallelograms.

Below are illustrations of two prisms.

 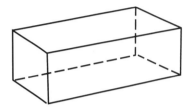

Find these prisms in the set of geometric models.

For each prism, identify the parallel and congruent faces.

Find other prisms in the set of geometric models.

How many others did you find? _____

Make a drawing of one of the prisms.

A **PRISM** can be named by the shape of the parallel and congruent faces.

Find the **TRIANGULAR PRISM**. Find the **HEXAGONAL PRISM**.

For a **RECTANGULAR PRISM**, every face is a rectangle. Find the **RECTANGULAR PRISM**.

Name the other prisms in the set of geometric models.

_____   _____

_____   _____

_____

A **PYRAMID** is a type of polyhedron. It is a solid figure with any polygon as a base. The lateral faces are always triangles. The triangles meet at a point called the **apex**.

Below is an illustration of a pyramid.

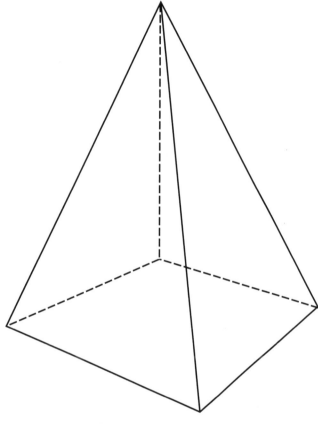

Find this pyramid in the set of geometric models.

Identify the base and find the apex.

Find other pyramids in the set of geometric models.

How many others did you find? _____

Make a drawing of one of the pyramids.

A pyramid can be named by the shape of the base.

Find the **TRIANGULAR PYRAMID**.

Find the **HEXAGONAL PYRAMID**.

Name the other pyramids in the set of geometric models.

_____

_____

How are pyramids different from prisms?

_____

_____

How are pyramids like prisms?

_____

_____

VERTICES, FACES AND EDGES FOR PRISMS

Find the prisms listed in the table below, and determine the number of **vertices, faces** and **edges** for each.

PRISM	VERTICES	FACES	EDGES
Rectangular Prism			
Triangular Prism			
Hexagonal Prism			
Octagonal Prism			
Trapezoidal Prism			
Square Prism (Cube)			
Oblique Square Prism			

How is the number of vertices for a prism related to the name of a prism?

____

How is the number of faces for a prism related to the name of a prism?

____

How is the number of edges for a prism related to the name of a prism?

____

Use your answers to find the number of vertices, faces and edges for a **PENTAGONAL PRISM**.

VERTICES: _____ **FACES:** _____ **EDGES:** _____

Can you find a relationship among the number of vertices, faces and edges for a prism?

____

____

Find the pyramids listed in the table below. Determine the number of **vertices, faces** and **edges** for each and record your answer in the table.

PYRAMID	VERTICES	FACES	EDGES
Triangular Pyramid			
Square Pyramid			
Hexagonal Pyramid			
Octagonal Pyramid			

How is the number of vertices for a pyramid related to the name of a pyramid?

_____

How is the number of faces for a pyramid related to the name of a pyramid?

_____

How is the number of edges for a pyramid related to the name of a pyramid?

_____

Use your answers to find the number of vertices, faces and edges for a **PENTAGONAL PYRAMID**.

VERTICES: _____   **FACES:** _____   **EDGES:** _____

Can you find a relationship among the number of vertices, faces and edges for a pyramid?

_____

How does this relationship compare to the relationship you found for a prism?

_____

A **REGULAR POLYHEDRON** is a polyhedron whose faces are all congruent regular polygons. Each face is congruent to every other face.

Historically, the Greek philosopher Plato attached one of the four "elements" (earth, air, fire, water) and the "universe" to a regular polyhedron. Therefore, the five regular polyhedra are called the **PLATONIC SOLIDS**.

Find the five Platonic Solids in the set of geometrical models.

Each regular polyhedron is named by the number of faces in the figure.

Below are illustrations of two Platonic Solids.

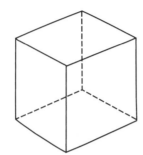 

The first one is called a **REGULAR HEXAHEDRON** because it has six faces. You can also name it as a cube or square prism. Plato associated this regular polyhedron with the **earth**.

The second Platonic Solid illustrated has 20 equilateral triangles as faces. It is called a **REGULAR ICOSAHEDRON**. Plato associated this regular polyhedron with **water**.

How many faces do each of the other Platonic Solids have?

_____   _____   _____

The names of these three Platonic Solids are **REGULAR TETRAHEDRON, REGULAR OCTAHEDRON** and **REGULAR DODECAHEDRON**.

Plato associated them respectively with **fire**, **air** and the **universe**.

What regular polygon is used for the face of each regular polyhedron?

_____   _____   _____

_____   _____

Select a vertex on each of the Platonic Solids. Note how many regular polygons meet at each vertex. What is the greatest number of regular polygons of each type that could meet at a vertex?

_____   _____

Find the models of the **RIGHT SQUARE PYRAMID** and the **RIGHT CIRCULAR CONE** in the set of geometric solids. If the **SQUARE PYRAMID** was sliced by a cut parallel to the square base, as illustrated in Figure 1, two pieces would be formed. One would be a smaller **SQUARE PYRAMID** as illustrated in Figure 2. The remaining solid is called the **FRUSTUM** of the square pyramid. It is illustrated in Figure 3.

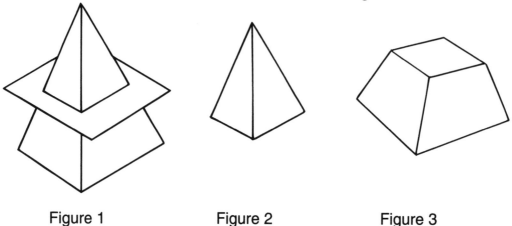

Figure 1   Figure 2   Figure 3

Find the model of the **FRUSTUM** in the set of solids. A **SQUARE PYRAMID** has five faces. It could be named as a **PENTAHEDRON**.

How many faces does the **FRUSTUM** have? _____

Name the **FRUSTUM** according to the number of faces. _____

In a similar way, if a **CONE** is sliced by a cut parallel to the circular base as shown in Figure 4, two pieces would be formed. One would be a smaller cone as shown in Figure 5, and the other solid would be the frustum of the cone as illustrated in Figure 6.

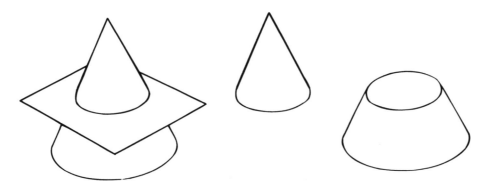

Figure 4   Figure 5   Figure 6

Find the model of the **FRUSTUM** of a cone in the set of geometrical solids.

Is it a cone? _____

Find the model of the **TRIANGULAR PYRAMID** in the set of geometric models. Sketch the **FRUSTUM** for this solid.

Name this **FRUSTUM** according to the number of faces it has.

_____

If a pyramid has **n** faces, then how many faces does the **FRUSTUM** of the pyramid have? _____

Describe the shapes of the faces of a **FRUSTUM** for any type of pyramid.

_____

_____

_____

The illustrations below show a **RECTANGULAR PRISM, RIGHT CIRCULAR CYLINDER, SQUARE PYRAMID** and a **CONE**.

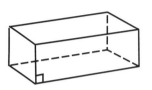 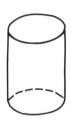 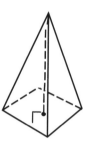 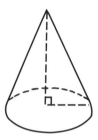

Find these four solids in the set of geometric models.

In the **RECTANGULAR PRISM**, the line segments connecting the congruent rectangular bases are perpendicular to those bases. Similarly, in a **RIGHT CIRCULAR CYLINDER**, the line segments connecting the congruent circular bases are perpendicular to those bases.

For the **SQUARE PYRAMID**, the line segment from the **apex** that is perpendicular to the base goes through the center of the square. In the same way, the line segment from the **apex** of the cone is perpendicular to the base and goes through the center of the circle.

Find the model illustrated below.

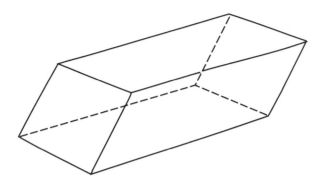

This is an example of an **OBLIQUE RECTANGULAR PRISM**.
The line segments connecting the congruent rectangular
regions are **not** perpendicular to the bases.

Find the model of an **OBLIQUE CIRCULAR CYLINDER**.
Describe why it is different from the **RIGHT CIRCULAR
CYLINDER**.

_____

_____

Find the model illustrated.

This is an example of an **OBLIQUE SQUARE PYRAMID**.
The altitude from the apex does **not** go through the center of
the square.

Find the model of an **OBLIQUE CIRCULAR CONE**. Describe
why it is different from the **RIGHT CIRCULAR CONE**.

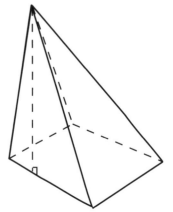

_____

_____

A polyhedron can be named in more than one way. Find the model of the polyhedron that is illustrated.

It could be named by considering the total number of faces – six. Therefore, the polyhedron is a **HEXAHEDRON**. Since all six faces are regular polygons, it is a **REGULAR HEXAHEDRON**.

This particular polyhedron is a **PRISM**. Prisms are named by the congruent polygonal faces that are parallel. Since the polygonal faces in parallel planes are squares, it could be called a **SQUARE PRISM**. You also know that this polyhedron is a **CUBE**. A square is a rectangle, therefore, a Square Prism is also a **RECTANGULAR PRISM**. Since a rectangle is a quadrilateral, you could also name it as a **QUADRILATERAL PRISM**.

Find this polyhedron in the set of geometric models.

Name it in two different ways.

_____

_____

Find this polyhedron in the set of geometric models.

Name it in two different ways.

_____

_____

Select other polyhedra and name them in more than one way.

_____

_____

_____

FIND THE SOLID

For each group of clues presented below, use the set of geometric models to find the figure described. Some groups of clues may describe more than one solid.

1.
- The solid has no faces.
- Every cross section is a circle.

_____

2.
- The solid has a volume that is one-third that of another solid.
- It has a base that is a square.

_____

3.
- The solid has congruent and parallel pentagonal faces.
- Its faces are all pentagons.

_____

4.
- The solid has exactly one circular face.
- It has exactly one vertex.

_____

5.
- The solid is not a pyramid.
- It has two congruent and parallel circular regions.

_____

6.
- The solid is a prism.
- It has six faces.
- Exactly two faces are isosceles trapezoids.

_____

7.
- The solid has twice as many edges as its base.
- Its faces are all triangles.

_____

8.
- The solid has an odd number of vertices.
- The number of sides for its base is not a square number.

_____

9.
- The solid has two similar and parallel faces.
- It has four trapezoidal faces.

_____

10.
- The solid has eighteen edges.
- It has four fewer faces than vertices.

_____

11.
- The solid has one more vertex than faces.
- It has exactly two triangular faces.

_____

12.
- The solid has exactly two faces that are parallelograms.
- The parallelograms are not rectangles.
- It has six faces.

_____

13.
- The solid has two congruent and parallel bases.
- A cross section parallel to a base produces a rectangular region.

_____

14.
- The solid has all triangular faces.
- It has more than four faces.
- It is not an icosahedron.

_____

15.
- The solid is a prism.
- It has ten faces.

_____

16.
- The solid has exactly one circular face.
- It has no vertices.

_____

EULER'S FORMULA

The relationship among vertices, faces and edges that you discovered for prisms and pyramids is known as **Euler's Formula.** Leonard Euler (1707-1783) was a Swiss mathematician who rediscovered the relationship about 100 years after the French mathematician, René Descartes, discovered it.

Letting **V** represent the number of vertices for a polyhedron, **F** the number of faces and **E** the number of edges, Euler's Formula can be written in symbols as:

$$V + F - 2 = E$$

Find the Platonic Solids in the set of geometric models. Complete the table below to determine if the relationship holds for the Platonic Solids.

PLATONIC SOLID	VERTICES	FACES	EDGES
Regular Tetrahedron			
Regular Hexahedron			
Regular Octahedron			
Regular Dodecahedron			
Regular Icosahedron			

Find this geometric model.

Does Euler's Formula work for this solid?

_____

Does Euler's Formula work for a

cylinder? _____ a cone? _____

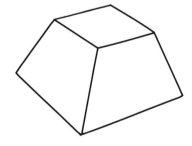

NAME CHANGE

The pyramids and prisms in the set of geometrical models have been named by the shapes of their bases. For example, a triangular prism has triangles for its bases, a square pyramid has a square as a base and a trapezoidal prism has trapezoids as bases.

Polyhedra are also named by the total number of faces that they have. A rectangular prism has six faces, so it can be called a **hexahedron**. Find the geometric models listed below. Name each one according to the number of faces it has.

NAME BY BASE(S)	NAME BY NUMBER OF FACES
Triangular Prism	
Hexagonal Prism	
Trapezoidal Prism	
Octagonal Prism	
Square Pyramid	
Hexagonal Pyramid	

What name could you give for the **frustum of a pyramid**?

_____

The pyramid and prism listed below are not in the set of models. Can you name them by the number of faces?

OCTAGONAL PYRAMID _____

PENTAGONAL PRISM _____

Look at the pair of names for each prism. How are the names related? Look at the pair of names for each pyramid. How are the names related?

_____

_____

_____

DIHEDRAL ANGLES

A **DIHEDRAL ANGLE** is the union of two half-planes and the common line defining the half-planes. The half-planes are called the **faces** and the common line is called the **edge** of the dihedral angle. A dihedral angle is illustrated below.

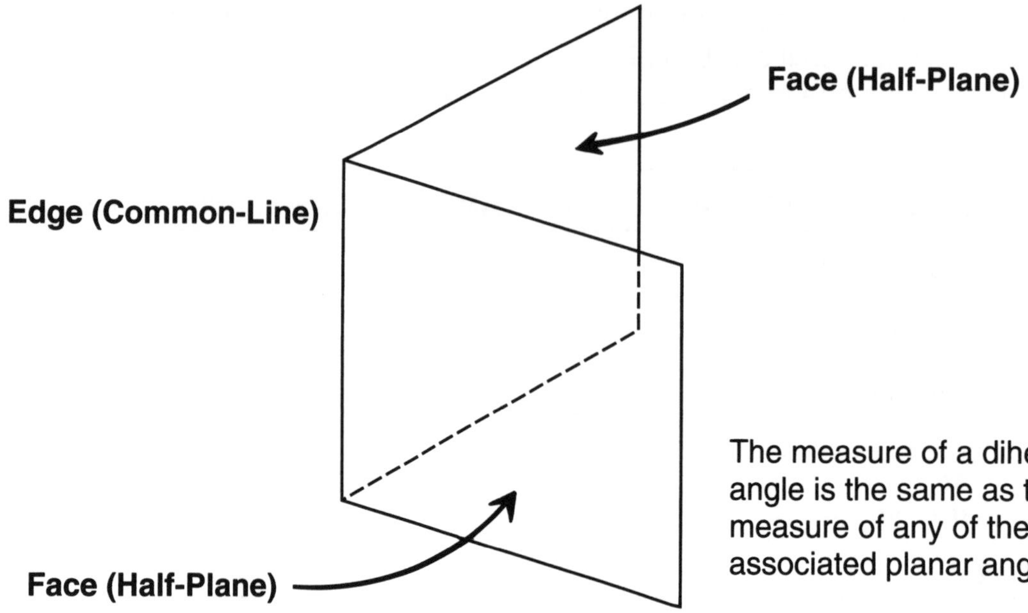

Face (Half-Plane)

Edge (Common-Line)

Face (Half-Plane)

The measure of a dihedral angle is the same as the measure of any of the associated planar angles.

Find the rectangular prism in the set of geometric models. How many dihedral angles are formed in the prism?   _____

What is the measure of each dihedral angle?   _____

Find the regular tetrahedron in the set of geometric models. How many dihedral angles are formed?   _____

What is the measure of each dihedral angle?   _____

Find the parallelepiped in the set of geometric models. How many dihedral angles are formed?   _____

For this solid, the dihedral angles do not all have the same measure. Use a protractor to measure each dihedral angle. Record your results below.

1. _____ 2. _____ 3. _____

Find the geometric solids listed below. Determine the measure of each different dihedral angle. Use a protractor if necessary. Record your results in the table.

POLYHEDRON	MEASURE OF DIHEDRAL ANGLES	
Cube	90°	
Triangular Prism		
Hexagonal Prism		
Octagonal Prism		
Triangular Pyramid		
Square Pyramid		
Hexagonal Pyramid		
Octahedron		
Dodecahedron		
Icosahedron		

A diagonal of a polygon connects two non-adjacent vertices. An **interior diagonal** of a rectangular prism connects two vertices of bases that are not in the same plane as the faces.

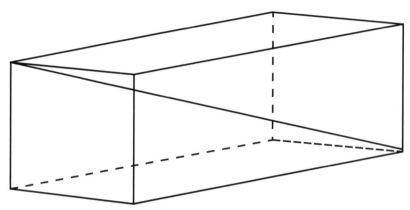

How many **interior diagonals** does a rectangular prism have? _____

Finding the length of an interior diagonal is a two-stage process. We will eventually create a formula for any rectangular prism.

Start with a **cube** from the set of geometric solids. The length of each side is _____ cm. Notice from the illustration below that an interior diagonal forms the hypotenuse of a right triangle.

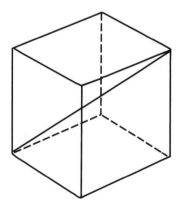

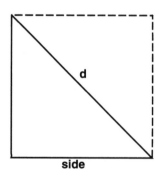

One leg of the right triangle is the side of the cube, while the other leg of the triangle is a diagonal of a square face. So, first find the length **d** of the diagonal of the square using the Pythagorean Theorem:

$$d = \sqrt{5^2 + 5^2} = \sqrt{50} = 5\sqrt{2}$$

INTERIOR DIAGONALS OF
RECTANGULAR PRISMS

continued

investigating
THREE-DIMENSIONAL
geometry

21

Now, use the Pythagorean Theorem again to find the length of the interior diagonal.

$$D = \sqrt{(5\sqrt{2})^2 + 5^2} = \sqrt{75} = 5\sqrt{3}$$

What is the relationship between the length of a side of a cube and the length of the diagonal of a square face? _____

_____

What is the relationship between the length of a side of a cube and the length of the interior diagonal of a cube?_____

_____

Use this relationship to find the length of the interior diagonal of a cube that has a side of length: 3 units. _____, 4 units _____, x units _____.

Now, find the length of the interior diagonal for the rectangular prism in the set of geometric solids. What are the dimensions of the prism?

Length: l = _____   Width: w = _____   Height: h = _____

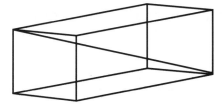 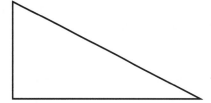

Again, the interior diagonal is the hypotenuse of a right triangle with one leg being a side of the prism and the other leg being the diagonal of a face.

Find the length of the face diagonal using the Pythagorean Theorem. **d =** _____

Now, use the Pythagorean Theorem once more to find the length **D** of the interior diagonal. **D =** _____

Suppose the dimensions of the prism were 2 x 3 x 4 units. What is the length **D** of the interior diagonal?

D = _____

Suppose the dimensions of the prism are **a x b x c**.

What is the length **D** of the interior diagonal?

D = _____

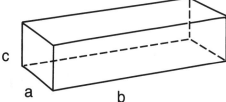

A diagonal of a prism is a line segment determined by two vertices that do not lie in the same face. In the illustration of the rectangular prism below, one of the diagonals is shown.

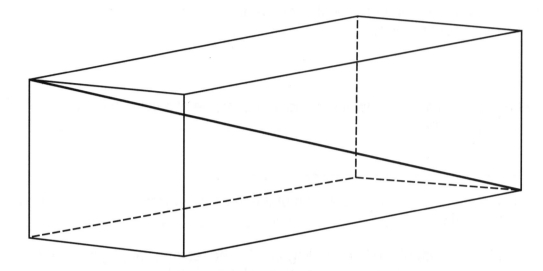

How many diagonals does a rectangular prism have?_____

Find the prisms in the set of geometric solids. Determine the number of diagonals for each, and record your result in the table below.

Look for a pattern in order to complete the table for prisms that are not in the set.

PRISM	NUMBER OF DIAGONALS
Triangular	
Rectangular	
Pentagonal	
Hexagonal	
Heptagonal	
Octagonal	
Nonagonal	
Decagonal	

SIMILARITIES AND DIFFERENCES

There are many different characteristics or attributes for the shapes in the set of geometric models. Sort the shapes into two or more groups. Describe how you sorted the models. What are the similarities of the shapes in each group? What are the differences between or among the groups?

_____

_____

_____

Sort the shapes in a different way. Again, describe how you sorted the models.

_____

_____

Find all the solids that have at least one triangle for a face. Sort these shapes into two or more groups. Describe the similarities for each group. Describe the differences between or among the groups.

_____

_____

Find all the solids that have at least one circle for a face. Describe how this group of shapes is different from the remaining shapes.

_____

_____

Find all the solids that have trapezoids as faces where the trapezoids have exactly one pair of parallel sides. Describe the similarities and differences among these solids.

_____

_____

Illustrated below are examples of a **RIGHT SQUARE PYRAMID** and a **RIGHT CIRCULAR CONE**. Every right pyramid and every right circular cone has two different heights that must be distinguished. First, there is the **height** of the pyramid or cone. This is the perpendicular distance from the apex of the pyramid or cone to the center of the base.

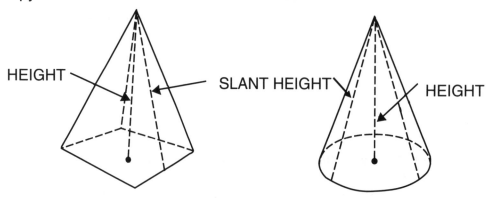

HEIGHT   SLANT HEIGHT   HEIGHT

Second, there is the **slant height** of the pyramid or cone.

For a pyramid, each lateral face is a triangle. The slant height for a pyramid is the altitude of the triangular face. All slant heights for a pyramid will be the same length if the base of the pyramid is a regular polygon.

For a right circular cone, the slant height is the line segment connecting the apex of the cone to any point on the circular base.

Use a ruler to find the height and slant height of the right square pyramid and right circular cone. Measure to the nearest millimeter.

RIGHT SQUARE PYRAMID	RIGHT CIRCULAR CONE
HEIGHT = _____	HEIGHT = _____
SLANT HEIGHT = _____	SLANT HEIGHT = _____

Find the height and slant height for each of the right pyramids in the set of geometric models.

How would you find a slant height for the **OBLIQUE SQUARE PYRAMID?**

_____

_____

The **Total Surface Area for a Prism** is the sum of the areas of all the faces. Certain prisms have special formulas for finding the total surface area.

Find the **CUBE** in the set of geometric models.

Each face of the **CUBE** is a square
Find the length **s** of one side of a square.

Record your measurement below.

s = _____   A = _____

The area of a square can be found using the formula $A = s^2$. Find the area of the square and record it above.

Since a **CUBE** has six congruent square faces, the **Total Surface Area** can be found by:

Total Surface Area (TSA) = $6s^2$

What is the **Total Surface Area** of the **CUBE** from the set? **TSA = _____**

A **RECTANGULAR PRISM** has six faces that are rectangular regions. There are three pairs of congruent rectangular regions. Look at the rectangular prism illustrated below, with length **l**, width **w** and height **h**.

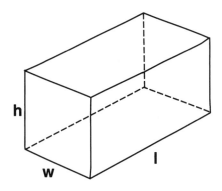

26 investigating
THREE-DIMENSIONAL
geometry

TOTAL SURFACE AREA
FOR PRISMS
continued

The three rectangles and their respective dimensions are shown.

w	h	h
l	l	w

A = lw   A = lh   A = wh

Since there are two of each rectangular region, the formula for total surface area of a rectangular prism is:

$$TSA = 2lw + 2lh + 2wh$$

Find the rectangular prism in the set of geometric models. Measure and record the length, width and height of the prism.

l = _____   w = _____   h = _____

Find the total surface area of the prism. **TSA =** _____

A general formula can be used to find the total surface area of **any** prism. Recall that a prism has at least one pair of parallel and congruent faces, called bases, while the remaining faces are parallelograms.

Find the **Triangular Prism** illustrated
to the right in the set of geometric models.

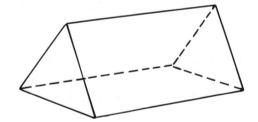

The equilateral triangle regions are parallel and congruent; the other faces are parallelograms, actually rectangles. The **Total Surface Area** formula for this prism is:

TSA = 2 x Area of Triangular Base + Sum of Areas of 3 Parallelograms

Find the **Total Surface Area** for the **Triangular Prism. TSA =** _____

TOTAL SURFACE AREA
FOR PRISMS
continued

Find the **Hexagonal Prism** illustrated to the right in your set of geometric models.

The hexagonal regions are the bases, which are parallel and congruent; the other faces are parallelograms (rectangles). The total surface area formula is:

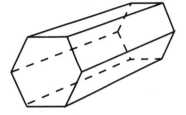

TSA = 2 x Area of Base + Sum of Areas of 6 Parallelograms

Note that the general formulas for triangular prisms, rectangular prisms, hexagonal prisms or any prism are the same.

TSA = 2 x Area of Base + Sum of Areas of Parallelograms

Now find the total surface area for each prism in the set of geometric models.

NAME: _____	**NAME:** _____
TSA = _____	**TSA =** _____
NAME: _____	**NAME:** _____
TSA = _____	**TSA =** _____
NAME: _____	**NAME:** _____
TSA = _____	**TSA =** _____

The total surface area for a pyramid is the sum of the area of the base and the areas of all the remaining triangular regions. Find the **RIGHT SQUARE PYRAMID** in the set of geometric models. The base is a square.
What is the length of a side? **s** = _____
What is the area of the base? **A** = _____

Each triangular face looks like the illustrated triangle. The altitude of each triangle is the slant height of the pyramid. Use a ruler to measure the slant height.

Slant Height = _____ **cm**

Now, find the area of a triangular face.

A = _____

Since there are four triangular faces, the total surface area will be four times the area you just found, plus the area of the square base.

What is the total surface area of the right square pyramid?

TSA = _____

Find the **TRIANGULAR PYRAMID** in the set of geometric models. Describe how to find the total surface area of this solid.

_____

_____

_____

Find the total surface area of the triangular pyramid.

TSA = _____

Find the total surface area of the hexagonal pyramid.

TSA = _____

Find the **SPHERE** in the set of geometric solids. The formula for the surface area of a sphere requires the higher mathematics of calculus to develop. It is given by

$$TSA = 4\pi r^2$$

where **r** is the radius of the sphere.

Find the radius of the sphere. **r** = _____

Find the total surface area of the sphere using 3.14 as an approximation for π

$$TSA = \text{_____}$$

Suppose you had a sphere whose radius was double that of the sphere in the set. Find the total surface area for this sphere.

$$TSA = \text{_____}$$

What is the relationship between the two values?

Find the **HEMISPHERE** in the set of geometric models. A **HEMISPHERE** is one-half of a **SPHERE**, but the total surface area is not one-half of the total surface area of a **SPHERE.**

Write a formula to find the total surface area for a hemisphere.

$$TSA = \text{_____}$$

Now, use your formula to find the total surface area for the model.

$$TSA = \text{_____}$$

Find the model of a **cylinder** in the set of geometric solids. A cylinder has three surfaces: two circular regions that are bases and a "curved" region connecting the bases.

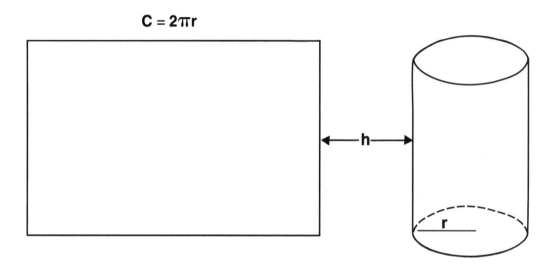

$C = 2\pi r$

The area of a circular region is found by using the formula $A = \pi r^2$, where **r** is the radius of the circle.

Determine the radius of the circular region for the cylinder: **r** = _____

Now, find the area of a circle, using 3.14 as an approximation for π

A = _____

So, **2A** = _____

If "unwrapped," the curved surface of a cylinder would have the shape of a rectangle. The height of the cylinder is one dimension of this shape. The other dimension is the circumference of the circular region, where $C = 2\pi r = \pi d$.

Find the circumference, using 3.14 as an approximation for π

C = _____

What is the area of the rectangle?

A = _____

What is the total surface area of the cylinder?

TSA = _____

Now write a formula for the total surface area of any right circular cylinder.

TSA = _____

The surface area of a cone is the sum of the lateral area and the area of the circular base. Find the **cone** in the set of geometric models. If the radius of the circular base is **r**, then the area of the base is $A = \pi r^2$.

What is the length of the radius of the base? **r =** _____ **cm**

What is the area of the circular base?
Use 3.14 as an approximation for π

$A =$ _____ $\textbf{cm}^2$

The shape of the lateral surface is a sector of a large circle. Cut out the jacket pattern for the cone on page 39.

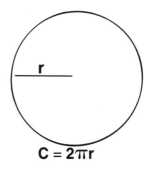

$C = 2\pi r$

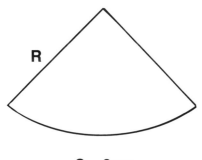

$C = 2\pi r$

Let **R** represent the radius of the sector. The length of the arc for the sector is $2\pi r$, the circumference of the circular base of the cone.

The area of the circle with radius **R** is $A = \pi R^2$, and the circumference of the large circle is $C = 2\pi R$.

32 investigating
THREE-DIMENSIONAL
geometry

SURFACE AREA
OF A CONE
continued

Now, we need to find the area of the sector. By constructing the proportion below, we can find the lateral surface area.

$$\frac{\textbf{Area of Sector}}{\textbf{2}\pi\textbf{r}} = \frac{\pi\textbf{R}^2}{\textbf{2}\pi\textbf{R}}$$

So, the area of the sector is **A = πrR**.

The radius **R** can be expressed in terms of the radius **r** and the height of the cone. In the right triangle illustrated below, **R** represents the slant height of the cone, **h** represents the height of the cone, and **r** represents the radius of the circular base.

By the Pythagorean Theorem, **$R^2 = r^2 + h^2$**. So **R = $\sqrt{r^2 + h^2}$.**

Therefore, the area of the sector can be rewritten as

$$A = \pi r \sqrt{r^2 + h^2}$$

We can now write a general formula for the total surface area of a cone.

$$TSA = \pi r^2 + \pi r \sqrt{r^2 + h^2}$$

Find the lateral surface area of the cone in the set of geometric models.

A = _____ cm²

Find the total surface area of the cone.

TSA = _____ cm²

GEOJACKETS

GEOJACKETS or **NETS** are patterns that can be used to cover a solid figure in your set of geometric models. Often these two-dimensional patterns make finding the surface area an easier task. Find the geometric model for the geojacket that is illustrated. This jacket is not drawn to scale.

Cut out the actual geojacket that is on page 35. Fold it on the dotted lines and fit it around the geometric model.

Using the geojacket, find the surface area for the prism by counting squares.

SURFACE AREA =

_____

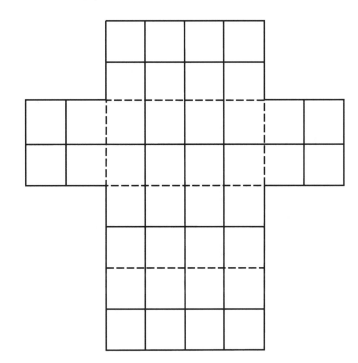

Find the geometric model illustrated below. Sketch a geojacket for the model.

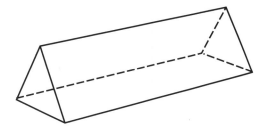

Now, cut out the actual geojacket on page 36 and then find the surface area of this model.

SURFACE AREA = _____

Find the **REGULAR TETRAHEDRON** in the set of geometric models. Sketch a geojacket for this model.

34 investigating THREE-DIMENSIONAL geometry

GEOJACKETS

**REGULAR
HEXAHEDRON (CUBE)**

GEOJACKETS

**RECTANGULAR
PRISM**

GEOJACKETS

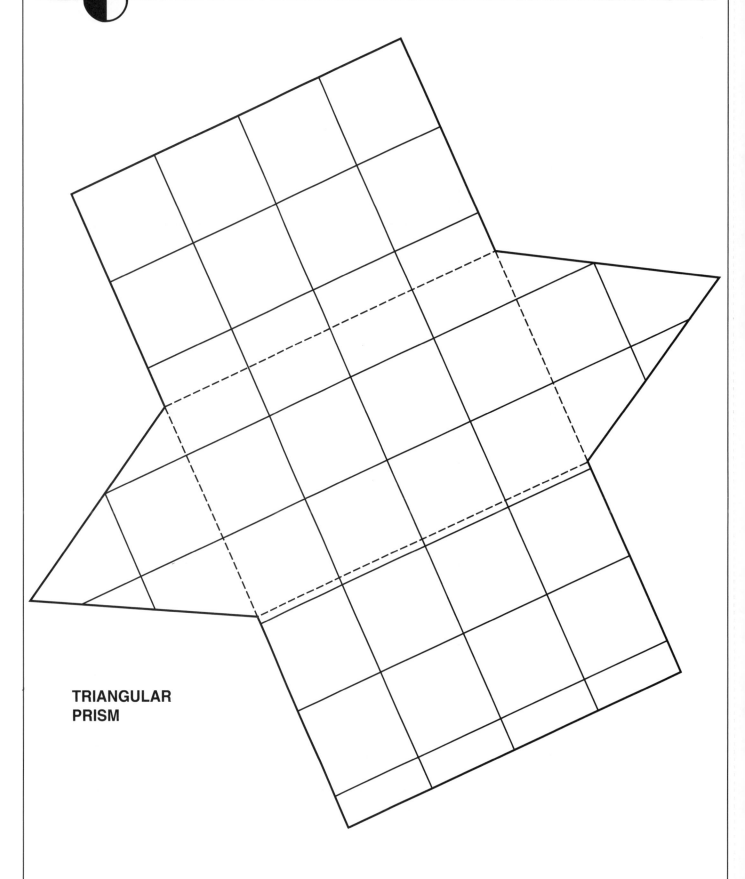

**TRIANGULAR
PRISM**

GEOJACKETS

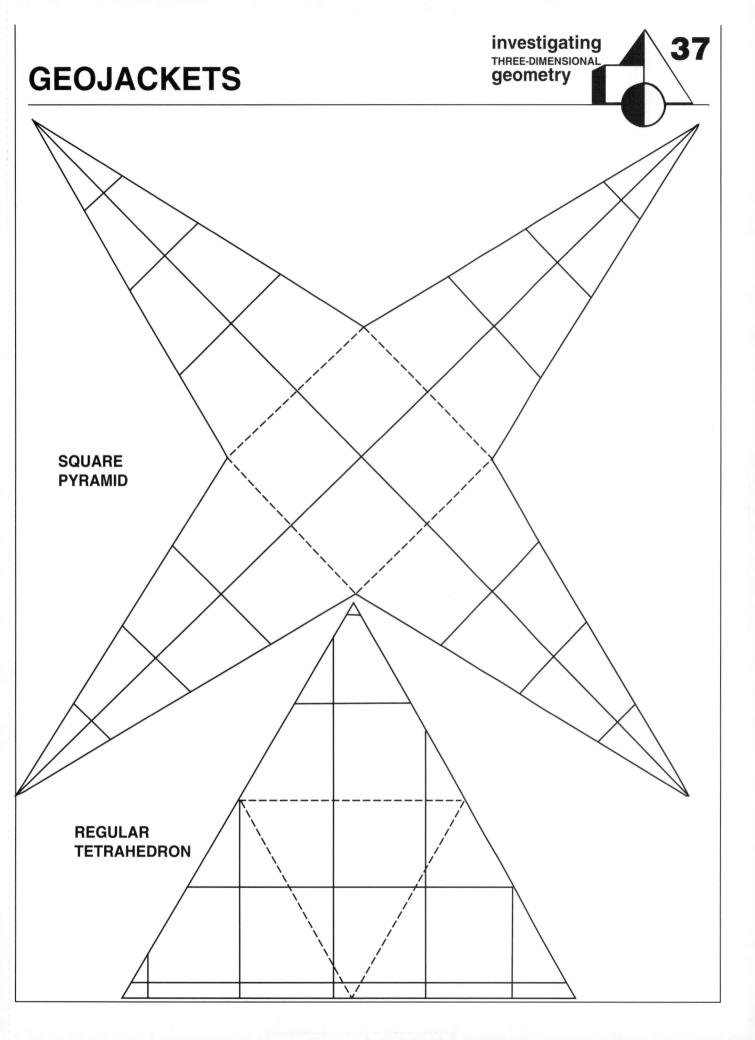

**SQUARE
PYRAMID**

**REGULAR
TETRAHEDRON**

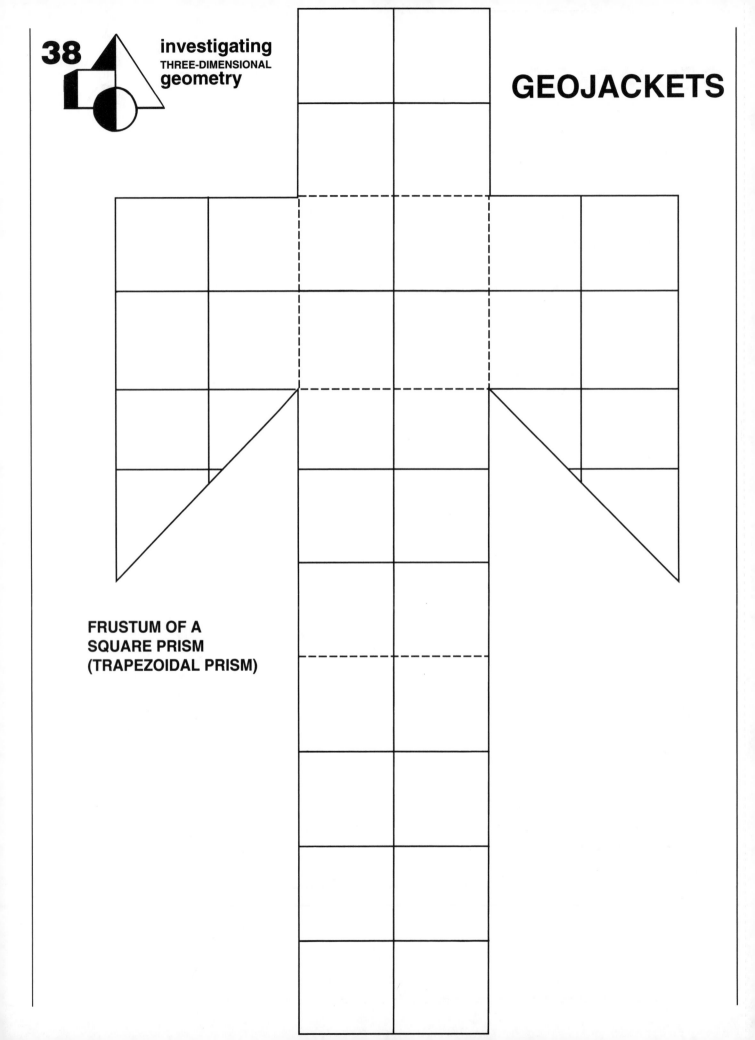

38 investigating THREE-DIMENSIONAL geometry

GEOJACKETS

**FRUSTUM OF A
SQUARE PRISM
(TRAPEZOIDAL PRISM)**

GEOJACKETS

CYLINDER

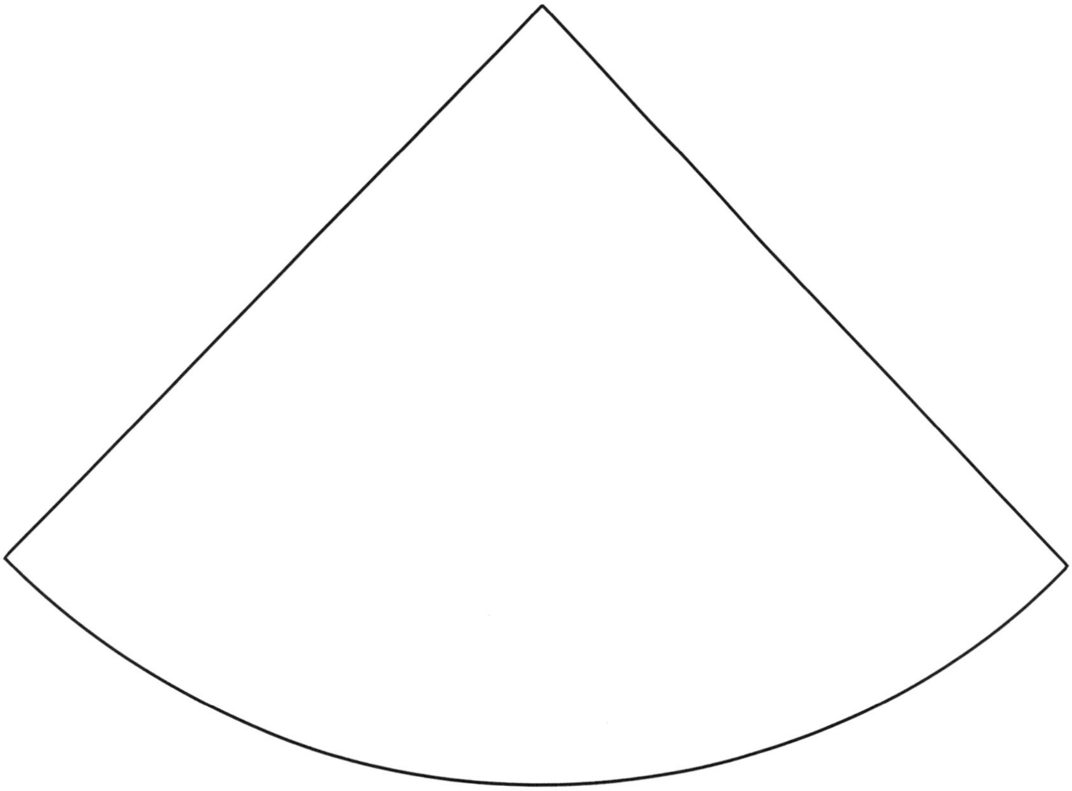

CONE

investigating
THREE-DIMENSIONAL
geometry

GEOJACKETS

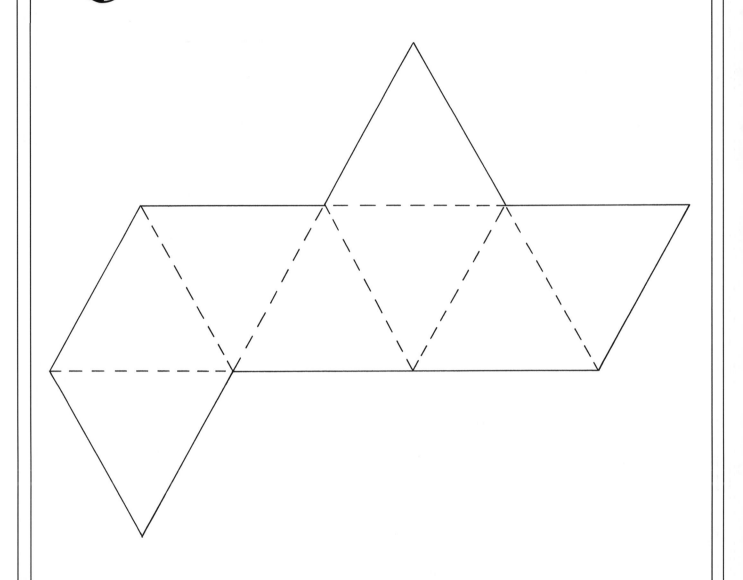

**REGULAR
OCTAHEDRON**

GEOJACKETS

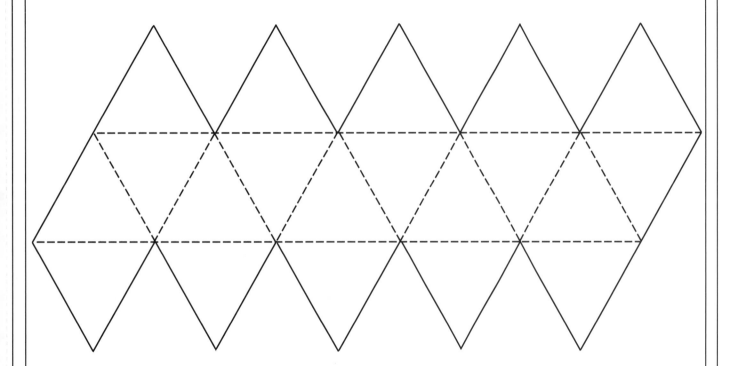

**REGULAR
ICOSAHEDRON**

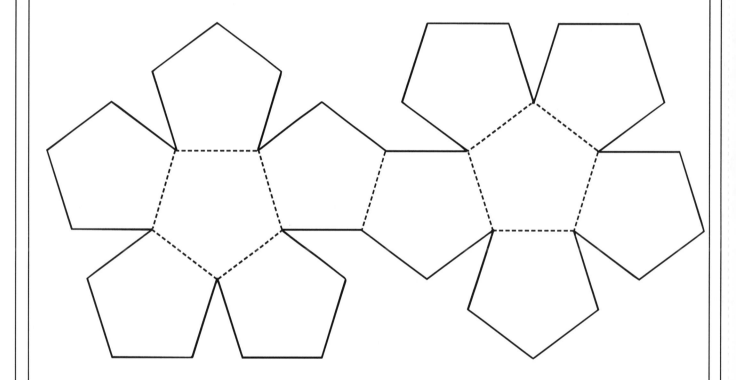

**REGULAR
DODECAHEDRON**

The **VOLUME** of a three-dimensional figure is the number of cubic units contained in the figure. Find the **CUBE** in the set of geometric models. What are the dimensions of the **CUBE**?_____

The illustration below shows a cube with each face marked off into squares. The number of small cubes contained in the large cube is 27 or 3 x 3 x 3. Therefore, the volume of this cube is 27 cubic units.

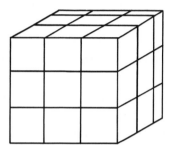

For any cube with a side of length **s**,
the volume can be found using the formula: $V = s^3$

Note that $s^3 = s^2 \times s$. The value of s^2 is the area of the base of a cube, while **s** is the height of the cube. So we could write the volume in words as:

Volume = Area of Base x Height

Suppose the length of a side of a cube is doubled, from **s** to **2s**. What is the volume of this new cube? **V** = _____. What is the relationship between the volume of the new cube and the volume of the original cube?

_____

_____

Now, find the **RECTANGULAR PRISM** in the set of geometric models. What are the dimensions of the prism? **l** = _____   **w** = _____   **h** = _____

The volume is the number of cubic units contained in the prism. The formula is:

V = l x w x h

What is the volume of the **rectangular prism**? **V** = _____

Note that **l x w** is the area of the base, so again we could write the volume of a prism in words as:

V = Area of Base x Height

44 investigating
THREE-DIMENSIONAL
geometry

VOLUME OF A PRISM
AND A CYLINDER
continued

Find the **TRIANGULAR PRISM** in the set of geometric models. Describe how to find the volume of this solid.

_____

_____

What is the volume of this prism? **V =** _____

Find the **CYLINDER** in the set of geometric models. The process for finding the volume of a cylinder is the same as that for prisms. However, the base of a cylinder is a circle.

What is the formula for the area of a circle? **A =** _____

Describe how to find the volume of the **CYLINDER**.

_____

_____

Find the volume of the **CYLINDER**. **V =** _____

Find another **PRISM** in the set of geometric models.

Find the volume of the **PRISM**. **V =** _____

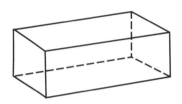
Find the **RECTANGULAR PRISM** and the **CIRCULAR CYLINDER** in the set of geometric models. The general formulas for the volumes of these two figures are similar.

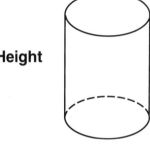

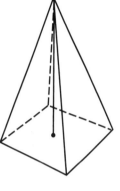

V = (Area of Circular Base) x Height

V = (Area of Base) x Height

For any prism, the general formula is:

V = (Area of Base) x Height

Now, find the **RIGHT SQUARE PYRAMID** and the **RIGHT SQUARE CONE** in the set of geometric models. Note that the base and height of each is the same as the rectangular prism and cylinder.

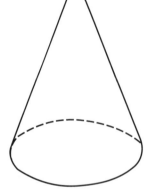

The **General Formulas** for the volume of the pyramid and the cone are the same:

V = 1/3 x Area of Base x Height

Find the volume of the square pyramid.

Height = _____   Area of Base = _____   V = _____

Find the volume of the cone.

Height = _____   Area of Base = _____   V = _____

Find the volume of the **HEXAGONAL PYRAMID** in the set of geometric models. Since the base is a regular hexagon, you can use the formula from page 2 to find the area of the base.

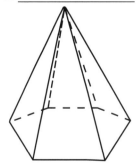

Height = _____   Area of Base = _____   V = _____

VOLUME OF A SPHERE AND A HEMISPHERE

Find the **SPHERE** in the set of geometric models. Determining the formula for the volume of a sphere requires using the higher mathematics of calculus. The formula is given below:

$$V = 4/3\ \pi r^3$$

What is the radius of the model? **r** = _____

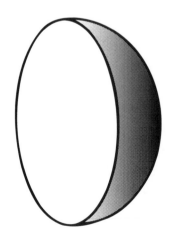

Find the volume of the sphere, using 3.14 as an approximation for π.

V = _____

Suppose the radius of the model was doubled. What is the volume of this sphere?

V = _____

How does the volume of the new sphere compare to the volume of the original sphere?

_____

Suppose the radius of a sphere is **x**. What is the volume of the sphere?

V = _____

If the radius is doubled to **2x**, what is the volume of the sphere?

V = _____

Find the **HEMISPHERE** in the set of geometric models.

What is the volume of the hemisphere?

V = _____

A **Stellated Polyhedron** is a polyhedron that is made "star-like" by placing pyramids on each face of the polyhedron. Below is an illustration of an **octahedron** and a **stellated octahedron**. Each of the eight triangular faces has a triangular pyramid attached.

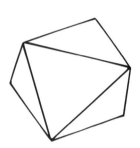
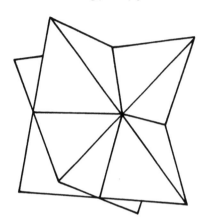

The five **Platonic Solids** are usually the polyhedra that are stellated. On the pages that follow are patterns to make the pyramids for each face of each **Platonic Solid**. Cut them apart, fold and tape together. Then carefully tape them to each face of a **Platonic Solid**.

Does **Euler's Formula for Solids** still hold? Check each **Platonic Solid** and record your results in the table below.

NAME	VERTICES	FACES	EDGES
Stellated Tetrahedron			
Stellated Hexahedron			
Stellated Octahedron			
Stellated Dodecahedron			
Stellated Icosahedron			

STELLATED TETRAHEDRON

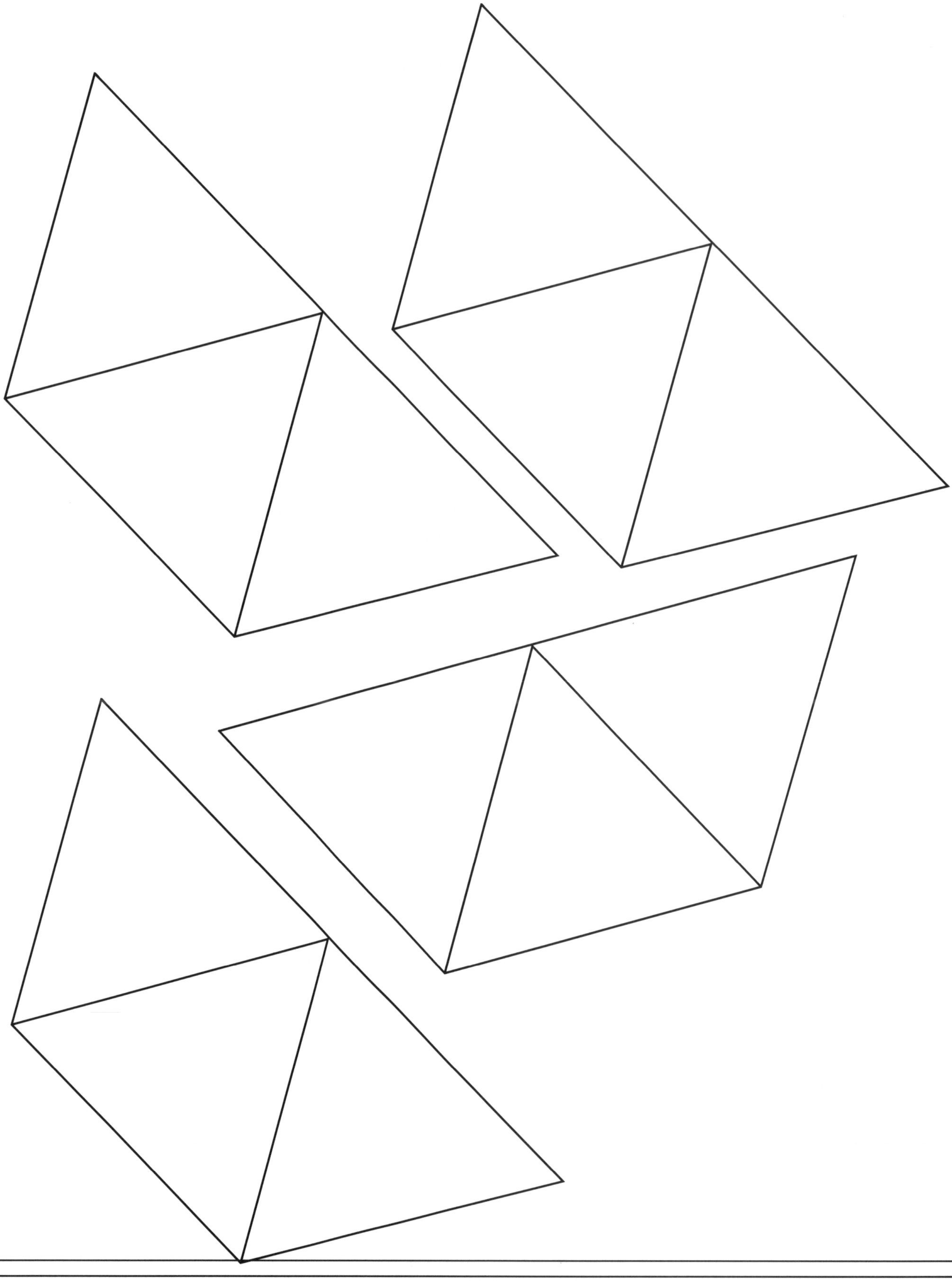

STELLATED HEXAHEDRON

investigating
THREE-DIMENSIONAL
geometry

STELLATED
OCTAHEDRON

DIFFERENT VIEWS

When you look at three-dimensional figures from different views, you often see different two-dimensional figures. Find the **RECTANGULAR PRISM** in the set of geometric models. Place it in front of you with one edge on the line segment below.

_____

If you look at the prism from the front, what shape do you see?

_____

If you look at the prism from the top, what shape do you see?

_____

If you look at the prism from the right side, what shape do you see?

_____

Find the **SQUARE PYRAMID** and place one edge of the base on the line segment below.

_____

If you look at the pyramid from the front, what shape do you see?

_____

If you look at the pyramid from the right side, what shape do you see?

_____

From the top, you should see a shape like the one illustrated on the right.

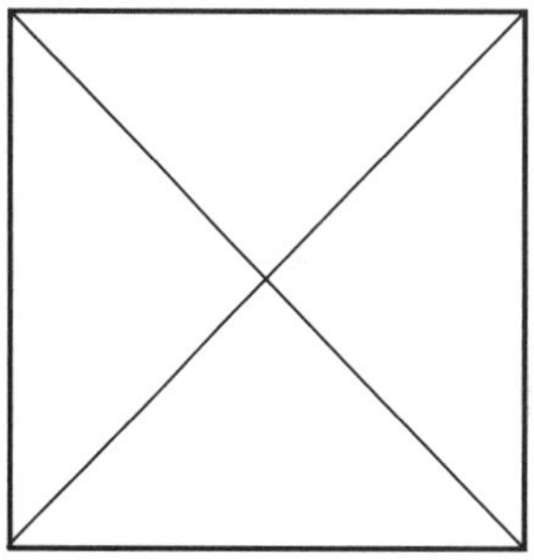

Illustrated below are the top, front, and right side views of one of the solids from the set of geometric models. Find the model.

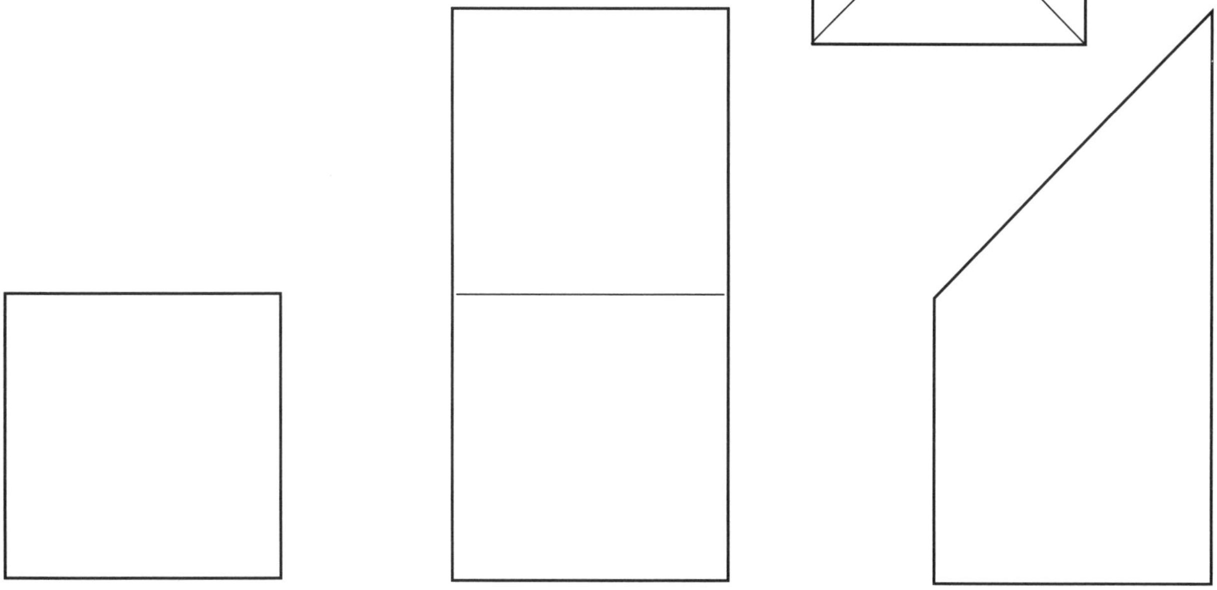

TOP

FRONT

SIDE

Shown on this page and pages 55 and 56 are the top, front and right side views of several solids from the set of geometric models. Find the model for each set of views, and write its name on the line.

TOP

FRONT

SIDE

1. _____

TOP

SIDE

FRONT

2. _____

DIFFERENT VIEWS
continued

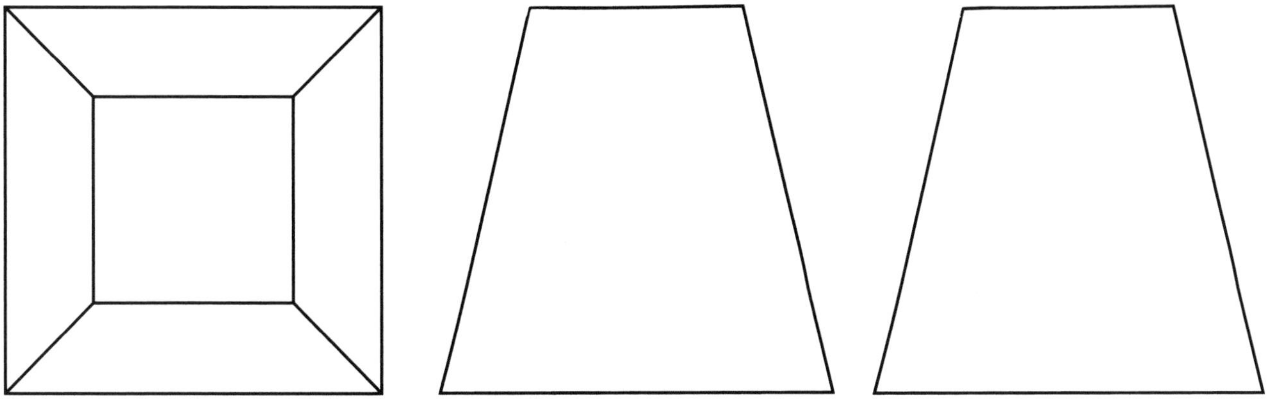

TOP

FRONT

SIDE

3. _____

TOP

FRONT

SIDE

4. _____

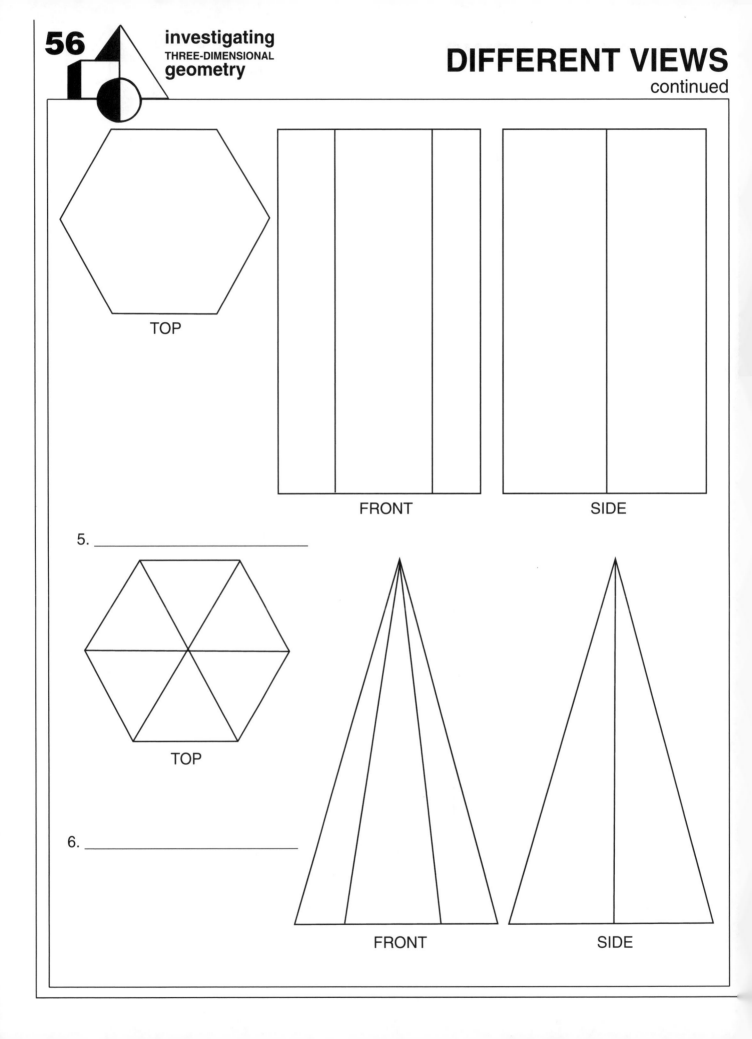

TOP

FRONT

SIDE

5. _____

TOP

6. _____

FRONT

SIDE

CROSS SECTIONS

When geometric solids are sliced or cut, a variety of plane regions are created. Determining what shape a region will have is easy for certain solids and cuts, but difficult for many others.

Find the **CUBE** in the set of geometric models.
When a slice is made that is parallel to a face of the cube, a square region appears.

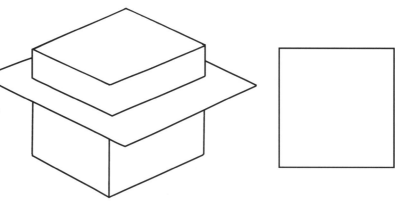

Now, visualize a slice that cuts off one vertex of a cube. Sketch the resulting region that you see.

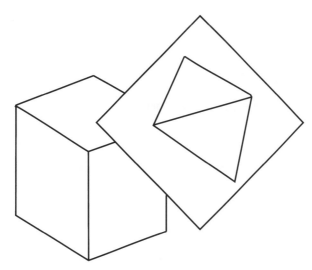

Describe how you could slice the cube to obtain other regions?

_____

_____

_____

How many different regions could you find? _____

Find the **CYLINDER** in the set of models. There are three types of cuts that could be made, each resulting in a different plane region. Name, if you can, the resulting region for the slices listed.

1. **A slice parallel to the base:** _____

2. **A slice perpendicular to the base:** _____

3. **A diagonal slice:** _____

Find the model that shows the region for a diagonal slice. What happens to the shape of the region as the slice gets closer to a parallel slice?

_____

_____

Find the **SQUARE PYRAMID** in the set of geometric models. Name, if you can, the resulting region for the slices listed.

1. **A slice parallel to the base:** _____

2. **A slice perpendicular to the base through the apex:**

_____

3. **A slice perpendicular to the base, not through the apex:**

_____

4. **A diagonal slice:** _____

5. **A slice cutting off a base vertex:** _____

Find the **CONE** in the set of geometric models. Name, if you can, the resulting regions for the slices listed.

1. **A slice parallel to the base:** _____

2. **A slice perpendicular to the base through the apex:**

_____

CROSS SECTIONS
continued

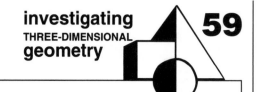

3. **A slice perpendicular to the base, not through the apex:**

   ____

4. **A diagonal slice:**______________________________

Select other figures from the set of geometric models. Visualize the resulting regions for slices similar to those that you have done.

NAME OF FIGURE	TYPE OF SLICE	REGION

Certain types of cuts (perpendicular to a base, cutting off a vertex or parallel to a base) always yield the same type of plane region. Write two or more statements about the resulting regions for each of the figures listed.

PRISM

____

____

____

PYRAMIDS

____

____

____

CUTTING CORNERS

The volume of a rectangular prism can be found using the formula:

$$V = l \times w \times h$$

Suppose you are given a 5 cm x 5 cm grid paper such as the one illustrated below.

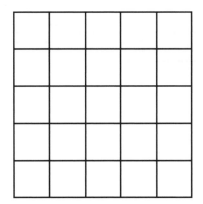 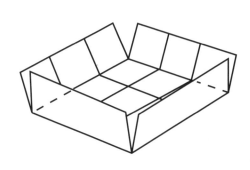

If you cut out the corner squares, the sides could be folded to form a box without a lid. What are the dimensions of this box?

l = _____ cm   w = _____ cm   h = _____ cm

What is the volume of this box? V = _____ cm³

Suppose you cut out a 2 cm x 2 cm square from each corner.
What are the dimensions of the box?

l = _____ cm   w = _____ cm   h = _____ cm

What is the volume of this box? V = _____ cm³

Since a 3 cm x 3 cm square cannot be cut from each corner, the greatest volume that you found was the volume for the second box that you formed.

CUTTING CORNERS
continued

Now, repeat the activity using a 10 cm x 10 cm grid found on page 63. First, cut out a 1 cm x 1 cm square from each corner. Fold the sides to form the box. Record the dimensions and the volume of the box in the table below. Next, cut out a 2 cm x 2 cm square from each corner of a new grid. Fold the sides to form a box. Record the dimensions and the volume of the box. Repeat the process until you have completed the table.

DIMENSION OF CORNER SQUARE	LENGTH	WIDTH	HEIGHT	VOLUME
1 x 1				
2 x 2				
3 x 3				
4 x 4				

What are the dimensions of the box that has the greatest volume?

Repeat this activity for a 15 cm x 15 cm grid.

DIMENSION OF CORNER SQUARE	LENGTH	WIDTH	HEIGHT	VOLUME
1 x 1				
2 x 2				
3 x 3				
4 x 4				
5 x 5				
6 x 6				
7 x 7				

CUTTING CORNERS
continued

What is the greatest volume that you found for this box?

$$V = \underline{\hspace{3cm}} \text{ cm}^3$$

Most often, the precise maximum or greatest volume of a box does not occur at the dimensions you have found. It occurs at some value close to the value you found.

For example, using the 5 cm x 5 cm grid, you found the greatest volume occurred when you cut out a 1 cm x 1 cm square from each corner. The volume of the box was 9 cm³.

However, suppose you cut out a square that was 5/6 cm x 5/6 cm. The dimensions of the box would be 10/3 x 10/3 x 5/6 and the volume of the box would be approximately 9.3 cm³.

Look at the dimension of the square cut from the corners of the 10 cm x 10 cm grid that gave the greatest volume. Select numbers greater than and less than this dimension. Use your calculator to find the volume of the box with these values. Compare the values to the greatest volume you found. List the dimensions of a square that gives a greater value.

_____

Repeat the activity for the 15 cm x 15 cm grid. List the dimensions of a square that gives a greater value for the volume.

_____

Try grids of other dimensions. Can you find a pattern for determining the dimension of the square to cut out that will give the greatest volume?

_____

_____

_____

10 cm x 10 cm grid

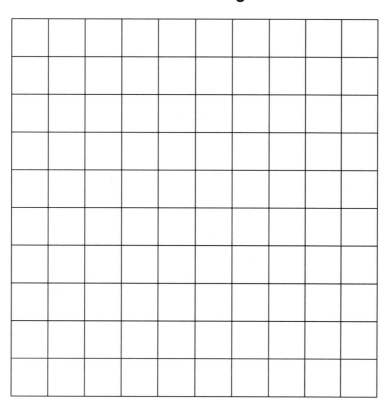

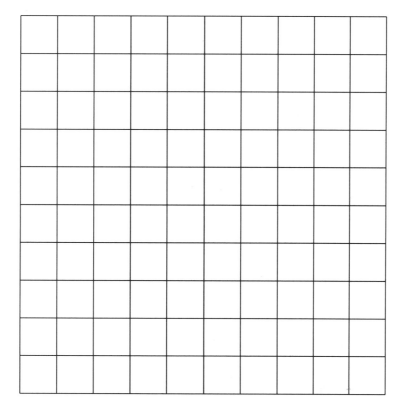

APPROXIMATE SURFACE AREAS AND VOLUMES OF SELECTED FIGURES

NAME	SURFACE AREA (cm²)	VOLUME (cm³)
Regular Tetrahedron	62.35	25.46
Regular Hexahedron	150.00	125.00
Regular Octahedron	86.60	58.93
Regular Dodecahedron	82.58	61.30
Regular Icosahedron	94.31	78.40
Triangular Prism	171.65	108.25
Rectangular Prism	250.00	250.00
Hexagonal Prism	223.30	216.51
Octagonal Prism	201.42	207.11
Square Pyramid	121.82	83.33
Hexagonal Pyramid	108.77	72.17
Cylinder	196.35	196.35
Cone	100.59	65.45
Sphere	78.54	65.45
Trapezoidal Prism	224.00	200.00
Frustum of Cone	131.72	229.07
Hemisphere	58.90	32.72
Oblique Square Pyramid	102.50	83.33
Parallelepiped	263.00	262.50
Frustum of Square Pyramid	107.75	72.92
Frustum of Square Prism	210.36	187.50